The Good Student

18. WELL
/20 DONE

Contents

Titles in the Runway series

Badger Publishing Limited
15 Wedgwood Gate, Pin Green Industrial Estate,
Stevenage, Hertfordshire SG1 4SU
Telephone: 01438 356907. Fax: 01438 747015
www.badger-publishing.co.uk
enquiries@badger-publishing.co.uk

The Good Student ISBN 978 1 84691 374 7

Text © Alison Hawes, Jonny Zucker 2008
Complete work © Badger Publishing Limited 2008

All rights reserved. No part of this publication may be
reproduced, stored in any form or by any means mechanical,
electronic, recording or otherwise without the prior permission
of the publisher.

The right of Alison Hawes and Jonny Zucker to be identified
as the authors of this Work has been asserted by them in
accordance with the Copyright, Designs and Patents Act 1988.

Publisher: David Jamieson
Commissioning Editor: Carrie Lewis
Design: Fiona Grant
Illustration: Anthony Williams, Robin Lawrie

Printed and bound in China through Colorcraft Ltd., Hong Kong

>The Good ___ Student

Written by Alison Hawes
Illustrated by Anthony Williams

Chen's dad had a restaurant.
Chen worked there at the weekends.

Mrs James liked Chen.
He was a good student.
He worked hard. He was polite and well behaved.

Mrs James didn't like Rob.
He didn't work hard.
He wanted to leave school.

One day, Mrs James saw that Chen and
Rob were friends.
Mrs James was worried.
She did not want Chen to become like Rob.

Then one day, Chen was late for class.
He had not done his homework.
Mrs James was very worried.

That night, Mrs James told her husband that Chen was becoming a bad student, like Rob.

Mr James told Mrs James not to worry.
He took her to Chen's dad's restaurant for
a meal.

Mrs James saw Chen working in the restaurant.

"Why are you working on a Friday, Chen?" asked Mrs James.

"My dad hurt his leg," said Chen.
"I have been helping him in the restaurant
this week."

"So, that is why Chen didn't have time to do his homework," said Mrs James.

Mr and Mrs James enjoyed their meal.
They told Chen's dad it was very good.

"I have a new boy working in the kitchen on Fridays," said Chen's dad.
"He wants to be a chef."

"I think you know Rob," said Chen's dad.
"He will be a top chef one day. He is such
a good student."

Mrs James felt silly, and very sorry.

Night «
Light

Written by Jonny Zucker
Illustrated by Robin Lawrie

Arjun wanted to be a policeman when he was older.

"I want to be a policeman," he told his mum.

"I want to be a policeman," he told his dad.

"You will be too tired to do any job," said his mum.

"What do you mean?" asked Arjun.

"You stay up too late reading," said his dad.

"Okay," said Arjun, "I will stop staying up late."

That night Arjun turned his light off at nine o'clock. "Good," said his dad. "Now get some sleep."

But when Arjun's dad was gone, he pulled out his torch from under the bed.
He read his book with the torch until it was very late.

The next day Arjun was very tired.
"You look very tired," said his mum.

"You can't be a policeman if you're always
tired," said his dad.

That night Arjun read with his torch until
late. But in the night he woke up.
He heard a sound outside the house.

Two men were standing outside.
They had a bag of tools.
They were trying to break in.

Arjun grabbed his phone and called the police.
Two minutes later he heard a police car.
The burglars started to run.

Arjun shone his torch in their faces.
The beam of light hurt their eyes.
They could not see anything.

The police car stopped.
Two policemen jumped out.
The policemen grabbed the burglars.

The policemen were very pleased with Arjun.
"I want to be a policeman when I'm older,"
said Arjun.
The policemen gave Arjun a booklet about
the police.

"It's too late to read that tonight," said Mum.

"Up to bed and lights out," said Dad.
Arjun said goodbye to the policemen.

"You could read that tonight," whispered one of the policemen.
"You could use that torch!"

Vocabulary «««

The Good Student

restaurant
polite
well behaved
worried/worry
homework
become
working
helping
enjoyed

Night Light

policeman
torch
outside
minutes
burglars
beam
booklet
whispered

>>> Story questions

The Good Student

When did Chen normally work in the restaurant?
Why did Mrs James like Chen more than Rob?
Was Rob a bad student?
Was Mrs James being fair?

Night Light

What does Arjun want to be?
Why is he always tired?
How did Arjun stop the burglars?
What do you think a job with the police would be like?